HOW TO GET ENGAGED

Questions to ask BEFORE you get engaged to be married.
Answering the question, "Should we get married?"

Bobb **BIEHL** *And* *Cheryl* **BIEHL**

Married Since 1964

HOW TO GET ENGAGED

Questions to ask BEFORE you get engaged to be married.
Answering the question, "Should we get married?"

Bobb BIEHL *And* *Cheryl* BIEHL

Married Since 1964

Written permission must be secured from the publisher
to use or reproduce any part of this book, except for brief
quotations in critical reviews or articles.
Biehl, Bobb.

Published by Aylen Publishing
P.O. Box 1999
Mt. Dora, FL 32756

ISBN 978-0-9765040-9-2

CONTENTS

There are few areas of married life which cause more yelling, pouting, and throwing of things than the financial area. One of the most frequent reasons given for divorce today is financial struggles and disagreements. If you are making different financial assumptions today – you will likely go through your marriage with some severe strains.
   • Credit Cards
   • Current Realities
   • Dreaming Of Some Day
   • Managing Our Money
   • Life Style / Standard Of Living
   • Spending Our Money
   • Who Makes The Money?

With one life mate decision, you are not only marrying a person, you are determining: your future mother-in-law, your future father-in-law, your children's grandparents, your children's other parent ...
   • Activities / Celebrations
   • Children
   • Concerns / Conflict Resolution / Skeletons
   • Extended Family Relationships
   • Former Marriages
   • Good Times
   • Intimacy
   • Lifestyle

- Responsibilities / Chores Around The House
- Time
- Values / Preferences
- What If ...

Remember back ten years. Talk about what life was like for each of you then. Could you possibly have imagined where you would be today? It would have been just as easy for you to imagine today ten years ago as it would be to imagine ten years from now...today!

Point: You will both continue to grow. How do you each want to grow, and in what direction?
- Books
- Dreams
- Growth Areas
- Issues
- Progress!
- Road Blocks To Growth
- Strengths

One basic reality in life is: We all change physically as we grow older. What are your thoughts about your own physical appearance and that of your life partner? How do you actually feel about your weight, your sex appeal, and your overall image?
- Aging
- Doctors
- Exercise
- Food
- Health
- Image
- Weight

As a person matures he / she moves through professional phases like:
"I got the job!"
"I think I'll choose this field as my profession."
"My career is progressing well ... or, in a slump."
"What will my lifework be?"
It is critical you are making the same basic assumptions concerning your work!
- Ambitious?
- Career
- Ideal Work?
- Mobility
- Salary Or Commission?
- Set Backs
- Significance
- Success
- Two Careers?

Friendships are invaluable! Social times are priceless! Are you making the same assumptions about your social life? Do you really enjoy the same people, the same parties, or entertaining in the same way?
- Changing Friendships
- Current Friends
- Entertaining Friends / Family
- Evenings Out
- Parties
- Past Relationships
- Social Confidence / Comfort
- Travel

Politics and religion are two taboos of polite conversation. In marriage, however, these topics are "must discussions!" Take some time and discuss each of these questions as openly as possible. Ten years from now, you will be very pleased you did!
- Bible

- Church
- Prayer
- Questions Of God?
- Spiritual Life
- Tithe
- Truth
- Your Personal Beliefs

  A. Turning Disagree Answers To Agree
  B. "Marriage is a covenant relationship not a contract"
      – John F. Huff
  C. Ten Very Predictable Problems
  D. Keeping Your Marriage Healthy And Happy
  E. Avoid:
  F. Rekindling Your Romance
  G. "You can know you are going to heaven when you die"
      – Tom Stebbins

  H. Conclusion – Invite us to your fiftieth anniversary party!

INTRODUCTION

A. *"Daddy, How can I know I'm in love?"* *"I'm getting married ... !"*

One day my much loved daughter came to me and asked, "Daddy, how can I know I'm in love?" After doing the very best a dad can do to answer her questions it became obvious this is a question thousands of young daughters are wrestling with every single day of the year.

About a week later a young man – age 22 – who lived just a few houses down the street stopped me on my way home and announced proudly, "Bobb, I'm getting married!"

"Great!" I responded. "May I ask you a quick question? ... how do you know this is exactly the right young lady for you?"

He answered very confidently, "Oh, we have so much in common!"

Like what?" I probed.

"Oh, everything!"

"Everything like what?"

"Oh, everything .... we like the same movies .... we both like tennis .... and, ... and, ... and ... Bobb do you think we should get married?"

"I have no idea if you should get married. But, if all I had in common was movies and tennis ... I'd sure get to know her a lot better before committing to spend the rest of my life with her" was my only advice.

Just two weeks later we met on the street and of course I asked, "How are the wedding plans coming?"

"Oh, we aren't even dating any more!"

"Why?"

"We just decided we just don't have enough in common!"

At that moment we developed a commitment to writing this book. We wanted to give young couples a list of questions we wished someone had suggested to us. We went back and thought of all of the heated discussions we had as a couple and turned each into a question to help you think through before a heated discussion ... what you would do if such a situation came up in your life.

Since our marriage we have done literally thousands of hours of
marriage counseling with couples who did not ask enough questions of each
other before getting married ... and, were now wishing they had.

We sincerely hope these questions help you know if you truly love each
other ... and, if you should get engaged ... to be married for life!

B. Pre-ENGAGED questions

BEFORE

you ask, "Will you marry me?" or, respond, "Oh YES!"

Is the wisest time

to do your PRE-MARRIAGE COUNSELING

AFTER

you get ENGAGED and,

the wedding dress has been ordered

IS FAR TO LATE for any hope of OBJECTIVITY.

200+ Fun questions

To help you get to know your POSSIBLE fiancé at an even deeper level, Cheryl and I have created more than 200+ fun questions that can clarify, deepen, and strengthen your relationship. These questions cover most of the major problem areas you are likely to face as a couple.

In creating these questions we have remembered our counseling sessions with couples soon to be married, happily married, and unhappily married. We have recalled discussions in our own marriage. We remembered happy times, sad times, explosive times, loving times, and resolution times. Then, we created questions we wish someone had suggested we ask each other before we got married.

The questions are divided alphabetically among seven basic areas of life:

1. Financial
2. Marriage and Family
3. Personal Growth
4. Physical
5. Professional
6. Social
7. Spiritual

These seven categories have been listed alphabetically, but this is not to imply the first on the list (financial) is more important than the last (spiritual). Note that God is not limited to the spiritual category. God is the God of families, commerce, hearts, minds, bodies, businesses, and societies, as well as the Lord of His church. So feel free to bring up the spiritual element in the discussion of any of the other categories.

A flexible approach to the process:

Start with the first alphabetically listed category (financial) and proceed down the questions one by one until you have answered them all. Then go to the next category and do the same. Don't forget to mark each question **Agree, Differences, OR... Disagree**.

Decide together if one of the seven areas particularly interests you at the moment (you do not have to start with financial). Start with the first question and work your way down, marking each one **Agree, Differences, OR... Disagree**. There is plenty of space so you can make notes in the book about your thoughts.

Answer three questions (or however many you decide) in one category. When those questions have been marked **Agree, Differences, or Disagree**. Then go to the next chapter and do three questions from that category. After you have answered three from each category, go back and answer three more from each category, and so on.

However you do it, we strongly suggest in each category of life you follow the questions in order. By doing so, you eliminate the frustration of trying to find the "perfect" next question.

If you come to a question that does not apply to your relationship, just skip it and move on. Or, if a question seems too sensitive to discuss, mark it Disagree and come back to it later.

As you answer each of the questions, you will undoubtedly think of additional questions. Write them down in the margin before you forget them.

Ask each other these questions to avoid divorce level conflict after you get married and build a strong understanding from the beginning

Make doubly sure your assumptions are compatible today, and you will be half as likely to divorce tomorrow! If either of you simply will not discuss any question, or section – you can count on major problems in that area at sometime in the future!

C. The **Agree / Differences / Disagree** system

It is critical to find "land mines" before they explode! The more you know about how your POSSIBLE fiancé thinks and feels about a wide variety of issues and the more discussions you have before you get ENGAGED or married, the fewer explosions you will encounter after you get married. After honestly discussing the questions in this book, there will be far fewer marriage-threatening surprises after you have announced your engagement or the minister proudly says, "May I present Mr. and Mrs. _____."

These questions uncover differing assumptions that might otherwise have become invisible, emotional "land mines" which explode unexpectedly and cause major damage to a relationship. These questions provide a "shovel" to dig out the hidden mines before you step on them. The best time to decide whether you will live the rest of your life together is before your engagement and certainly before the "I do," not after! It is hard but far easier to break a dating relationship than an engagement. It is far easier to break an engagement than a marriage after the vows have been spoken and children have been conceived or born.

We do not wish to put unnecessary stress on a relationship, but rather simply to bring to light those areas in which there is existing agreement or disagreement. This then gives you opportunity to enjoy fully your agreements and to explore fully your disagreements, before the ring – the announcements, the engagement parties and certainly before your final "Till death do us part."

As you discuss the questions in this book, you may find only three or four that are potentially relationship-threatening disagreements. Work through these potentially explosive areas during the "deeply in love" part of your relationship, when you are eager to "work things out".

Suppose, however, you don't discuss these issues until after you are married, possibly have children, and increased financial obligations. If a problem arises and one of these areas of disagreement must be faced under pressure, it creates a situation in which a marriage can blow apart and end in divorce. The devastation of divorce is what these questions are designed to prevent.

Agree / Differences / Disagree

A great way to communicate your agreement, or lack of agreement, on each question is the "Agree / Differences / Disagree" technique. After you have discussed a question, check one of three symbols:

👍 ◯ 👎   Thumbs up symbol is Agree
        Easy / total agreement!

👍 ◯ 👎   The Circle is Differences
        Different conclusions or misunderstanding – don't agree –
        need to talk and see if we are actually disagree or agree.

👎 ◯ ☝ Thumbs down symbol is Disagree

Absolutely deadlocked – totally disagree ...

could be a "deal breaker"!

There are no "right" or "wrong" answers. The issue is whether or not you agree, not who is right.

When you finish the material, expect to have many agrees in each of the sections, a few Differencess, and hopefully very few Disagrees. Once a question is agree, you may want to use a agree marking pen or pencil to highlight those questions so you can see at a glance how much you already agree. It's satisfying and reassuring!

If you disagree on a question, the first thing you ask is, "Is this an important issue to me? To us?" If your difference of opinion is on something both of you consider unimportant, you don't need to discuss it any further. Simply go to the next question and enjoy discovering more about each other.

Some of the questions do not require you to agree on an answer; you are just sharing personal experiences with each other. In that case, just mark it agree when you have finished your discussion.

Go back to the Differences questions and discuss them until they turn agree or disagree. Of the questions you mark Disagree, there may be only two or three that actually represent "divorce potential" kinds of conflict.

D. Talk it out / write it out

One of the advantages of these questions is you can simply talk them out. Depending on your personal preferences, you may even want to record some of your answers to listen to yourselves in twenty years. This will provide "great" memories for you, and it may be valuable for your sons and daughters to hear the thoughts and feelings of your dating years. If you are separated for a period of time because of career or school, you may want to write out your answers to certain questions and send / e-mail them to each other. In fact, this is a fun way to answer these questions even if you're in the same room.

Although it might sound like a lot of work, writing out your thoughts and feelings has many advantages:

- Writing gives you time to reflect on the questions
  and think more about your answers.
- You have a chance to present your answer in totality
  without the risk of being interrupted.
- Some people find it easier to write something very personal
  than actually say it out loud.

Whichever way you choose to discuss these questions, we hope you thoroughly enjoy the process, and the experience helps you both communicate your thoughts, feelings, dreams, and concerns clearly to one another.

E. You are about to make one of life's three critical decisions.

1. Life / Eternal Destiny

The single most important decision any man or woman ever makes is the decision that will reveal the determination of his or her eternal destiny.

If you are settled in this area ... great! If not, you may want to read in this book's APPENDIX: "You can know you are going to heaven when you die" – Tom Stebbins

2. Life Mate

The second most critical decision a person makes in an entire lifetime is with whom (if anyone) he or she will become a life partner, committed to live and to grow old together in marriage. Many lives are lived in happiness and many others are lived in misery based on the wisdom of this single decision.

This book is intended to maximize your marriage, not undermine it. Although some of the questions may seem threatening, look at them as an opportunity to learn more about yourself as well as your partner. As you both have a better understanding of each other, you will be able to handle the stresses that inevitably come in a marriage.

We are not for or against your getting married.

We are for your getting married –

    if it will last the rest of your life.

We are against your getting married –

    if it will not bring you a mutually satisfying relationship, and end

    in divorce.

3. Life Work

The third most critical decision we face in life is of our career and lifework, in view of eternity ahead of us and the life partner beside us.

In one sense, all of the other decisions and choices in life can be seen as reflections of these three critical decision points.

1. FINANCIAL

Financial Balance

When your outgo – exceeds your income
Your upkeep – will be your downfall!

There are few areas of married life which cause more yelling, pouting, and throwing of things than the financial area. One of the most frequent reasons given for divorce today is financial struggles and disagreements. If you are making different financial assumptions today – you will likely go through your marriage with some severe strains.

Discussing your financial assumptions will help reduce the amount of frustration, pressure, and tension you experience.

• **Credit Cards**

(Remember the three symbols are for ...

Thumbs up symbol is a **Agree**

Easy / total agreement!

The Circle is **Differences**

Different conclusions or misunderstanding – don't agree – need to talk and see if we are Disagree or Agree.

Thumbs down symbol is **Disagree**

Absolutely deadlocked – totally disagree ... could easily be a "deal breaker!"

What do you think about credit cards?

How many do you have now?

What is the balance on each?

Which cards should we have after marriage?

- **Current Realities**

  👍⭕👎 How much money do you make?

  👍⭕👎 Do you have any money saved?

  👍⭕👎 What are your total financial obligations right now?
  (Including all school debts etc.)

- **Dreaming of Some Day**

    👍 ◯ 👎   If we were financially independent and didn't need to work for money, what would you see yourself doing with your time?

    👍 ◯ 👎   If we inherited a million dollars, what would you want to do with it?

                If we got a bonus of $1,000, how would we spend it?

                $10,000? $100,000?

    👍 ◯ 👎   Is there something fun or special you've always wanted us to do, but we haven't yet had the money?

- **Managing Our Money**

  👍 ⭕ 👎   Do you see yourself as "competent or incompetent" to manage money / keeping financial records?

  👍 ⭕ 👎   Who will be responsible to see monthly bills are paid?

  👍 ⭕ 👎   Who will balance the monthly bank statement?

  👍 ⭕ 👎   What are your feelings about a monthly budget? Do we make the budget together?

  How much should we allow for each of us to have for personal money to spend any way we choose?

What percentage of our income should we

👍⭕👎   save?

👍⭕👎   give to the place of worship we attend? Why?

👍⭕👎   give to charitable organizations?

👍⭕👎   invest? How? When?

How do you feel about:

👍⭕👎   joint versus separate checking accounts?

👍⭕👎   borrowing money from our parents or relatives?

👍⭕👎   loaning money to our parents or relatives?

👍⭕👎   How much life insurance should we have? Health insurance? What company? Why?

👍⭕👎   Who should do the gift buying for birthdays? Anniversaries? Christmas? Other special days? If it's usually the same person, how can the other help?

👍⭕👎   What should be the dollar limit on purchases made without the other's knowledge? Why?

👍⭕👎   What are your feelings about a will? When do you think we should have a will? Why?

👍⭕👎 Imagine a friend of ours borrows money from us and doesn't repay it.

How would you feel? What would you do?

👍⭕👎 How do you feel about declaring bankruptcy

- **Life Style / Standard Of Living**

👍 ⭕ 👎   For the first year of our marriage, do you want to live in an apartment, condominium, house, mobile home, or tent? Why?

👍 ⭕ 👎   How much money should we spend on furniture the first year? Why?

👍 ⭕ 👎   Cash or credit card?

👍 ⭕ 👎   What are your feelings about buying good used furniture?

👍 ⭕ 👎   What furniture style do you prefer?

👍 ⭕ 👎   How expensive a house do you want to live in? In five years? Ten years? Twenty years (today's valuation)?

👍⭕👎 Will our income after marriage support the standard of living you've become accustomed to?
If not, what adjustments do we need to make?

👍⭕👎 What kind of car(s) would you like to drive after we get married? In five years? Ten years? Twenty years?

👍⭕👎 How much do you now spend per month on clothing?
How much should we spend on clothing during our first year of marriage?
How much would you like to spend a year in five years? Ten years?

👍⭕👎 How much should we spend a year on luxury items such as jewelry, athletic equipment, trips, etc.?

👍⭕👎 What percentage should we tip a server who does an outstanding job? An average job? A poor job?

👍 ⭕ 👎   How much should you have to pay to have your hair cut?

Styled?

What is a suitable tip for these services?

👍 ⭕ 👎   How much should we spend on a getaway weekend?

- **Spending Our Money**

    ♂○♀ How much should we spend on:

    - Birthdays: each other's, parents, children, friends, others (you name)

    - Anniversaries: our own, parents, friends, relatives

    - Other special days: Mother's Day, Father's Day, Valentine's Day

    - Christmas: each other's gift, parents, children, other relatives, coworkers, friends

    - Christmas decorations?

    ♂○♀ How would you have the most amount of fun if we only had ten dollars to spend some evening?

How much can we currently afford to spend on the following typical household items:

- Apartment / condominium / house

- Athletic equipment

- Bedroom furniture

- Cars

- Computers / technology

- Dining room furniture

- Dishwasher

- Food processor

- Hobby items

- Living room furniture

- Music system

- Musical instruments

- TV

- Washer / dryer

- Other:_____

- **Who Makes The Money?**

    👍 ○ 👎   How much income would you like us to make (together) during our first year of marriage?

    👍 ○ 👎   Do you see both of us working after marriage? If so, for how long?

Remember:

There are few areas of married life which cause more yelling, pouting, and throwing of things than the financial area. One of the most frequent reasons given for divorce today is financial struggles and disagreements. If you are making different financial assumptions today – you will likely go through your marriage with some severe strains.

Discussing your financial assumptions will help reduce the amount of frustration, pressure, and tension you experience after you are married.

DO NOT gloss over Disagrees in this area ... talk your potential fiance' into the agree range or seek outside help to get some objective marital counseling before getting ENGAGED!

2. MARRIAGE AND FAMILY

Generations

With one life mate decision, you are not only
marrying a person, you are determining:

    Your future mother-in-law
    Your future father-in-law
    Your children's grandparents
    Your children's other parent
    Your future nieces and nephews.

You are also deciding
    Where you, and your children, will likely spend
    Thanksgiving,
    Christmas, and
    birthdays for the next fifty plus years.

And,
    you are determining all future generations of your
    family for hundreds of years!

The success or failure of your marriage impacts a lot of people. Communicate honestly and clearly on these issues. Your extended family for generations to come will be influenced by your discussions and your decisions.

- **Activities / Celebrations**

    👍⭕👎   Describe your idea of an ideal week of evenings?

    What would you like to do Monday night? Tuesday, etc.?

    👍⭕👎   Do you want to do local or international volunteer work?

    👍⭕👎   What do you picture us doing on our first vacation?

    👍⭕👎   How do you want to celebrate our wedding anniversary
    each year (in general)?

- **Children**

　👍○👎　What three things do you expect to be most rewarding about parenting? The three most frustrating?

　👍○👎　Ideally, how many children would you want to have?

　👍○👎　Do you think we should both work full time after we have children?

　👍○👎　Do you have any preferences about how many boys? Girls? How many years between them?

　👍○👎　How do you think you would respond if we had a severely disabled child?

　👍○👎　What are your thoughts and feelings about future abortion? Past abortions?

👍⭕👎   What would you do if one of our children wanted to marry someone of another race or ethnic group?

👍⭕👎   How do you feel about birth control?

👍⭕👎   If you think we should use something, what method do you see as the best one for us?

👍⭕👎   How do you think you would feel if we were not able to have children?

👍⭕👎   In that case, how do you feel about adoption?

👍⭕👎   What are the top three things you definitely want me to do for and with our children?

👍⭕👎   What do you see as your role as a parent with our children? My role?

👍⭕👎 Do you think children should be paid for jobs around the house? Why? How much?

👍⭕👎 Do you think children should be given an allowance? If so, how much at ages five, ten, fifteen, twenty-one? If not, why not?

👍⭕👎 What would be the three most strictly enforced rules of our house for child discipline?

👍⭕👎 What three to ten foundational truths do you think should be stressed in the raising of children? How can we do that practically? What "field trips" do you want our children to experience?

👍⭕👎 What vacation trips with the family – learning experiences – do you want to take "for sure"!?

👍⭕👎 How often should we as parents get away from babies in their first year. How often when the children are older?

👍○👎 How do you feel about nursery schools?
About daycare centers? What are the advantages?
Disadvantages?

👍○👎 If it's a holiday and you want a new outfit,
and the baby also needs new clothing,
and you can only afford one, honestly who would get the
new outfit and why?

👍○👎 How much would you guess it costs to care for a baby per
month in the first year?
(You may want to double-check with a couple who has a
new baby, to see if you are in the "ball park.")

👍○👎 What style of discipline would you use with a toddler?
Elementary-age child? Junior high? High school?
College-age?

👍○👎 How do you feel about spanking a child? Under what
conditions? With what instrument?

👍 ⭕ 👎   What do you think about having our elementary-age children in Sunday School or church?

Junior high? High school?

👍 ⭕ 👎   Do you think elementary-age children should be in a public or private school?

What about home schooling? What about older children? Why?

👍 ⭕ 👎   At what age should a daughter / son begin to date? What should be our house rules for curfew?

👍 ⭕ 👎   How much of our child's college education should be paid by us? Under what conditions?

👍 ⭕ 👎   How much freedom and responsibility should children be given at age five? Ten? Fifteen?

👍⭕👎 How do you feel about male or female surgery to avoid having more children?
At what number of children,
or under what circumstances,
would you consider it necessary to take precautions not to have more children?

👍⭕👎 Are there areas in which we may be a bad example to our children? What can we do about this?

👍⭕👎 If we have children, would you prefer one of us staying stay home and raising them or hiring a nanny?

👍⭕👎 Who would be the primary disciplinarian?

- **Concerns / Conflict Resolution / Skeletons**

👍⭕👎 When we disagree with one another, how should we settle it?

👍⭕👎 What do you think about marital counseling? Why? What are the advantages? Done by whom?

👍⭕👎 Who could we talk to who would help us understand and deal with our concerns before we actually marry?

👍⭕👎 What are your three greatest concerns or lingering questions about our married life together?

👍⭕👎 Do you have any "unresolved" relationships with former friends?

Are there any "skeletons" / "struggles" of any kind in your past?

Abortions, alcohol or drug use / abuse, arrest(s), bankruptcy, divorce(s), gambling, pornography – etc.?

Avoid surprises after saying "I do."

Talk about these things before the final commitment, not on your honeymoon!

- **Extended Family Relationships**

  👍⭕👎   Deep down, how does your mother feel about our relationship? Your father? Brothers and sisters?

  👍⭕👎   What words would you use to describe your parents' marriage and relationship? Why?
  Your grandparent's marriage?

  👍⭕👎   What are the three things you admire most about each of your parents as a marriage partner?

  👍⭕👎   What are the three things you admire most about each of your parents as people?

  👍⭕👎   What changes would you want to make from your childhood in relation to raising our own family?

👍⭕👎 If one of our parents became widowed or seriously ill, what would you think should be our responsibility to him / her?

👍⭕👎 Do you foresee any of our relatives interfering in our marriage? Who? How?
What would we do if that happened?

👍⭕👎 How much time do you want to spend with our respective families?

👍⭕👎 How involved do you want them in our lives? Vacations, home life etc?

• Former Marriages

👍⭕👎   Have you been married before? If so, how many times?

👍⭕👎   How long were you married?

👍⭕👎   How long have you been separated?

👍⭕👎   What would you say was the main reason your marriage ended?

👍⭕👎   What were some of the main issues / areas of disagreement in your marriage?

👍⭕👎   Did you or your ex seek any counseling before mentioning divorce?
If so, which spouse suggested/went?

👍⭕👎   Where does the ex-spouse now live? Are they re-married?

👍⭕👎　How would you describe your current relationship with your ex?

Do you consider this the ideal arrangement? Why?

👍⭕👎　Are you still in communication with any of the ex-in-laws? To what extent?

👍⭕👎　Do you have any children from the former marriage?

How old are they? Where do they live?

How often do you see them?   Would you like to be with them more or less often?

How do you see me relating to them?

About, how much money do you spend on them (not counting any child support)?

👍〇👎 How do you handle seeing your ex in public situations?

How would you like me to handle any such meetings?

👍〇👎 Are there any remaining 'ties' resulting from that marriage:

Child custody / Child support?

Combined business ventures?

Credit card debt?

👍〇👎 Is your name on any items – with debt (vehicle / home) he / she is in possession of now?

👍〇👎 Are there any outstanding lawsuits with a 3rd party?

- **Good Times**

👍⭕👎 What are your three most positive expectations about our married life together?

👍⭕👎 What are three of your happiest memories of our life together so far? Why?

- **Intimacy**

What's involved in "romance" for you? How important to you are those elements in our marriage?

What are your three favorite thoughts about making love after we're married?

What are three assumptions you have about how I will make love?

What are your taboos or things you do not want to do at all in lovemaking?

From your perspective, what are the most important things to be aware of when making love?

Have you had a sexual relationship in the past – has it scarred you?

👍⭕👎   When was your last sexual relationship?

👍⭕👎   Do you struggle with porn? What are your feelings about pornographic magazines, movies, etc.?

👍⭕👎   What physical dimensions "turn you off" sexually? What "turns you on" sexually?

👍⭕👎   Specifically, what do you plan to do to avoid the potential of having an affair?

- **Lifestyle**

    👍⭕👎 How much television do you watch a week?

    Mostly what kind of programs do you watch?

    How do you feel about having the television turned on for most of the day?

    👍⭕👎 How do you feel about an unmade bed in the middle of the day?

    👍⭕👎 Are you a night person or a morning person?

    What time do you typically get up in the morning?

    How would you suggest we adjust?

    👍⭕👎 Are you organized and neat / clean at home?

    👍⭕👎 How often do you think a person should take a shower / bath?

    Brush teeth?

    Change the bathroom towels?

Vacuum and dust?

Wash out the tub?

👍⭕👎 How much do you want to travel together?

👍⭕👎 Do you want time to travel or go out by yourself or with friends but not together?

- **Responsibilities / Chores Around The House**

👍 ◯ 👎 How often do you feel it is important to go out to dinner rather than cook at home?

👍 ◯ 👎 Do you like cooking or want your spouse to cook – or share the kitchen – or alternate cooking?

👍 ◯ 👎 Who do you think is responsible to do the following work around the home?

_____ Bill paying

_____ Car repairs

_____ Putting up the Christmas tree

_____ Dishes

_____ Fixing things

_____ Grocery shopping

_____ House cleanin

_____ Ironing clothes

_____ Making the bed

_____ Washing clothes

_____ Doing yard work

Other _____

• Time

👍 ⭕ 👎 Do you need some alone time even after married – once a week or year etc? How much? When?

👍 ⭕ 👎 What would be the advantages of waiting one more year before getting married?
What would be the disadvantages?

👍 ⭕ 👎 How long do you think we should be married before having children?

👍 ⭕ 👎 Would you be open to people staying at our house? Living with us short term or long?

- **Values / Preferences**

  👍⭕👎 What does the phrase "Till death do us part" mean to you?

  👍⭕👎 Do you see divorce as an option in any circumstances? If so, in what circumstances?

  👍⭕👎 If there has been divorce in your immediate family, what preventive steps can we take to avoid similar disruptive patterns in our relationship?

  👍⭕👎 What couple, whom you know personally, has the most ideal marriage?
  Why do you think it is so ideal?

  👍⭕👎 Where do you want to live ideally? (area, state, country)

  👍⭕👎 Do you prefer to be at home together at night and weekends - or be with friends?

☝ ◯ 👇   What kind of music do you like? Dislike?

- **What If ...**

  👍 ○ 👎   What would you do if I became totally incapacitated and could never have sex or children?

  👍 ○ 👎   What would be your response if I broke my back and was partially paralyzed?

  👍 ○ 👎   What if our marriage doesn't turn out to be quite as much fun as you expected it to be?

  👍 ○ 👎   What if my job required me to be away from home a week or two at a time?
  Do you feel you could handle being alone that much without being tempted to "run around"?
  Do you feel I / you could handle being alone?

Remember:

With one life mate decision, you are not only marrying a person, you are determining:

> Your future mother-in-law

> Your future father-in-law

> Your children's grandparents

> Your children's other parent

> Your future nieces and nephews.

You are also deciding

> Where you, and your children, will likely spend

> Thanksgiving,

> Christmas, and

> birthdays for the next fifty plus years.

And, you are determining all future generations of your family for hundreds of years!

3. PERSONAL GROWTH

Dreams

> *Dreams*
> *help pull us through*
> *deep waters, pressure situations, exhaustion, sickness*
> *and many other forms of*
> *pain points.*
>
> *Keep growing into your own potential*
> > *and*
> > *your distant dreams*
> *to help keep you focused*
> *on positive possibilities*
> *not just*
> *current circumstances.*

Remember back ten years. Talk about what life was like for each of you then. Could you possibly have imagined where you would be today? It would have been just as easy for you to imagine today ten years ago as it would be to imagine ten years from now…today!

Point: You will both continue to grow. How do you each want to grow, and in what direction?

- **Books**

  👍○👎 What three books would you most like to read? Why?

  👍○👎 Name five of your all-time favorite books.
  What did you like about them? Would you like me to read them?

- **Dreams**

  👍⭕👎 If you could become the "world expert" in anyone area or subject, what would it be?

  👍⭕👎 Would you ever like to go back to school? What school? For what reason?

- **Growth Areas**

    👍⭕👎   A year from today, in what three areas of your life would you most like to be stronger?

    👍⭕👎   If you could sit and chat with any person in the world, with whom would you talk?
What three questions would you ask that person? Why?

    👍⭕👎   In what three areas would you most like to see me grow in the next year? Why?

    👍⭕👎   If we could improve only one aspect of the way we relate to each other, what would that be? Why?

- **Issues**

  👍⭕👎 What moral / social / political issues would you like to know more about? Why?

  👍⭕👎 What moral / social / political issues are you passionate about today? Why?

  👍⭕👎 Where would you like to volunteer time?

- **Progress!**

  👍 ◯ 👎 In what three areas of your life do you think you have grown most in the last several years?

  👍 ◯ 👎 What three people have had the greatest impact in your life? Why?

  👍 ◯ 👎 Who was your best friend in grade school? Junior high? High school? College?
  How did each contribute to your personal growth at that time of your life?

- **Road Blocks To Growth**

  👍 ⭕ 👎   What do you feel are the three key things keeping you from reaching your full potential today?

  👍 ⭕ 👎   What keeps you from getting excited about being promoted at work or taking on more responsibility? What negative comment did someone make about you years ago which is still holding back your confidence? How can I help you overcome that blockage in your life?

• Strengths

What do you consider your three greatest strengths to be maximized in the future?

Of all the things you do well ... what do you do the very best?

What is your single greatest strength?

Remember:

Dreams

help pull us through

deep waters, pressure situations, exhaustion, sickness

and many other forms of

pain points.

Keep growing into your own potential

and

your distant dreams

to help keep you focused

on positive possibilities

not just

current circumstances.

Do you share the same dreams?

4. PHYSICAL

Image

When you meet a man – you judge him by his clothes.

When you leave a man – you judge him by his heart.

– an ancient Russian proverb

One basic reality in life is: We all change physically as we grow older. What are your thoughts about your own physical appearance and that of your life partner? How do you actually feel about your weight, your sex appeal, and your overall image?

- **Aging**

  👍 ◯ 👎   How do you feel about getting older? Thirty? Forty? Fifty? Sixty? Seventy+?

- **Doctors**

  👍⭕👎 Would you prefer to go to a medical doctor or a
  nutritionist?

  👍⭕👎 How do you feel about going to chiropractors?

- **Exercise**

    👍⭕👎 How do you feel about an exercise program for you and me? What kind? How often?

    👍⭕👎 What kind of physical exercise would you most like to do together? Separately?

    👍⭕👎 Do you have a favorite recreational activity?
    How often do you participate in it now?
    Does it require continual updating of equipment?
    How much do you spend in a year on that activity?

- **Food**

  👍⭕👎 How do you feel about the food we eat?

  What changes would you make?

  Are you willing to help make changes (shopping, cooking, studying, etc.)?

  👍⭕👎 Do you prefer to eat healthy foods or not?

- **Health**

  👍○👎 How do you feel about taking vitamins and nutritional supplements?
  How much per month should be spent on them?

  👍○👎 Based on your family's medical history, do you have any anxieties about your health either now or in the future? How would you feel if I developed one of these conditions?

  👍○👎 Do you have any desire to belong to a health club, YMCA, or to a country club? Why?

  👍○👎 How do you feel about alcoholic beverages? Cigarettes? Pipes or cigars? Mind-altering drugs?

  👍○👎 How do you feel about the differences in our natural energy level?

- **Image**

👍◯👎   What five things do you like best about my physical appearance?

👍◯👎   What three suggestions would you like to make about how I can improve my physical appearance?

👍◯👎   How do you 'feel about baldness? Wrinkles? Gray hair?

👍◯👎   How do you prefer I wear my hair?

👍◯👎   How do you feel about beards, dread locks, mustaches, sideburns, tatoos etc.?

👍◯👎   How many buttons should I leave open on a shirt or blouse?

🖒◯🖓   What is your favorite outfit/clothing – for you and for me – why do you enjoy it?

🖒◯🖓   What three nationally known personalities do you most identify with and would most like to be like?

🖒◯🖓   Who are three national and visible personalities you find most attractive sexually, and what is it about them you find attractive?

🖒◯🖓   How will you deal with the difference between what you find attractive in others of the opposite sex and what I am not?

- **Weight**

  👍◯👎   How do you feel about me being overweight?

  👍◯👎   How do you feel about you being overweight?

  👍◯👎   How many pounds do you think is overweight for each of us?

  👍◯👎   What is your ideal weight? Mine?

Remember:

One basic reality in life is: We all change physically as we grow older.

What do you actually think / feel about your own physical appearance and of your life partner?

How do you actually feel about your weight, your sex appeal, and your overall image?

How do you feel about growing old together ... physically?

5. PROFESSIONAL

Work

An activity is only work –

if you would rather be doing something else!

As a person matures he / she moves through professional phases like:

"I got the job!"

"I think I'll choose this field as my profession."

"My career is progressing well ... or, in a slump."

"What will my lifework be?"

It is critical you are making the same basic assumptions concerning your work!

- **Ambitious?**

  👍 ◯ 👎   What will you have to know, do, or become to feel ready for your next promotion at work?

  👍 ◯ 👎   Do you see yourself working over-time after we get married?
  What time will you be going to work and coming home?

  👍 ◯ 👎   How would you describe your career ambitions?

  👍 ◯ 👎   To what professional or work-related associations or groups should you, or I, or we belong? Why?

- **Career**

👍⭕👎   What would you consider my top three alternative careers? Why do you think these would be good things for me to pursue?

👍⭕👎   How would you describe the difference between having a job, a profession, a career, and a lifework?

👍⭕👎   How important to you is our parents' acceptance of what I do as a profession?
Our children's acceptance?

👍⭕👎   If I had all the time, energy, and money I needed and could have any position or work, what position or work would you ideally like me to have? Why?
What position or work would you like to have?

👍⭕👎   What is the highest position you can imagine me holding at some time in the future?

👍 ◯ 👎   How would you feel about me if I became a:

❑   Corporate executive?

❑   Farmer?

❑   Factory worker?

❑   Lawyer?

❑   Medical professional (doctor, nurse, etc.)?

❑   Minister?

❑   Missionary?

❑   Movie star?

❑   Musician?

❑   Police officer?

❑   Politician?

❑   Psychologist?

❑ Salesperson?

❑ Self-employed?

❑ Truck driver?

❑ Other _____ (You name it!)

👍⚪👎 If the career I chose required me to spend three to ten years of preparation before I could become successful, how would you feel about waiting that long?

- **Ideal Work?**

  👍 ⭕ 👎 How do you feel about my work – your work?
  What do you like best about it?
  Is there anything about my / your work that frustrates or worries you?

  👍 ⭕ 👎 What type of work do you think I / you would do best?

  👍 ⭕ 👎 What do you consider the three most important factors in bringing you happiness or satisfaction in your work? How many of those factors are present in your work now?

  👍 ⭕ 👎 What brings you the most satisfaction in your job or career? In the relationships at work?

  👍 ⭕ 👎 What kind of work brings you personal fulfillment?

  👍 ⭕ 👎 How important is it to you to have fun at your work?

👍⭕👎 How important to you is being a member of the team at work? Of being accepted by that team?

👍⭕👎 How important is security in any career you would choose? Why?

👍⭕👎 Would you rather work with your hands, your head or your back?

👍⭕👎 If you could realistically have anyone's job in the world, whose job would you have and why?

👍⭕👎 What do you definitely not want in your work?

👍⭕👎 What is it in your work you would definitely not want me to be part of in the future?

👍⭕👎 How would you feel about me working a night shift?

👍⚪👎   How would you feel about me working two jobs?

- **Mobility**

  👍⭕👎 How do you feel about a job or career for me that would include travel?

  👍⭕👎 How much travel would be acceptable to you? How much would you find unacceptable?

  👍⭕👎 If my work responsibilities required me to move to another location, in what parts of the country / world would you feel comfortable living?
  Where would you definitely not want to live? Why?

  👍⭕👎 If my work required a move and yours did not, how would we decide what to do?

- **Salary Or Commission?**

  👍⚪👎 What company, organization, or firm would you most like to work with if you had your choice? Why?

  👍⚪👎 How would you feel about starting a business from scratch where there was a major risk to the money we invested from our savings?

  👍⚪👎 Would you prefer I be on a lower fixed salary or a higher potential commission with no guaranteed income? Why?

  👍⚪👎 If I decided to go back to school for further education, how would you feel about the decision?
  Why? What would be the advantages? Disadvantages?

  👍⚪👎 If you could start a business with anyone, what three people would you choose to be partners? Why?

👍◯👎 If we started a business together, what would you want to do in that business?

👍◯👎 Would you hesitate to start a business of our own? Why?

👍◯👎 Do you prefer to work for a firm or on your own?

• **Set Backs**

👍○👎 If you were ever fired from a job in which you were happy, how would you want me to relate to you when you came home from work?

👍○👎 How would you feel about me if,
after five years of working hard in some business or profession, I failed?

- **Significance**

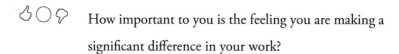 How important to you is the feeling you are making a significant difference in your work?

- **Success**

    👍⭕👎   What work-related or professional goals will you have to reach to feel really successful in life?

- **Two Careers?**

  👍⭕👎 How would you feel about my working with the company where you work?

  👍⭕👎 How would you feel about us working together as a two-person team at some time in the future?

  👍⭕👎 If you would feel good about that, what would you see us working on together?

  👍⭕👎 In your heart of hearts, how do you feel about a wife having a separate career from her husband,
  where she may need as much support to keep going in her profession as the husband?

  👍⭕👎 How would you feel about me making more (or less) money than you, if that should happen?

👍⭕👎 Under what circumstances do you feel a wife / mother should (should not) work outside the home?

👍⭕👎 While you were growing up, did your mother work outside the home?
Either way, how did you feel about it? Why?

Remember:

As a person matures he / she moves through professional phases like:

"I got the job!"

"I think I'll choose this field as my profession."

"My career is progressing well ... or, in a slump."

"What will my lifework be?"

It is critical you are making the same basic assumptions concerning your work!

6. SOCIAL

Friends

Be very careful the friends you choose –
for in fact you will be come more and more like them!

Friendships are invaluable! Social times are priceless! Are you making the same assumptions about your social life? Do you really enjoy the same people, the same parties, or entertaining in the same way?

- **Changing Friendships**

  👍○👎   What qualities do your friends have in common? What do you look for in a friend?

  👍○👎   What do you feel you give to a friendship?

  👍○👎   Where would you like to meet new friends in the future? (church, work, family, etc.)?

  👍○👎   How would you guess our social relationships with each of our current friends will change when we get married?

  👍○👎   One year after we're married, what differences would you anticipate in our social life?
  After five years?

- **Current Friends**

  👍⭕👎 Who are your three closest friends? Why do you enjoy
  them?
  How do you think I feel about them?

  👍⭕👎 Who are three people you used to have as friends but have
  drifted from?

  👍⭕👎 Why did those friendships drift apart,
  and how does it make you feel when you reflect on these
  faded friendships?

- **Entertaining Friends / Family**

  👍○👎 How do you feel about having friends "pop in"? Your relatives? My relatives?

  👍○👎 How do you feel about us "popping in" on friends? Your relatives? My relatives?

  👍○👎 How many nights a month would you be open to guests staying in our home?

  👍○👎 How do you feel about your parents' social life? How do you feel about my parents' social life?

- **Evenings Out**

  👍⭕👎   What do you enjoy most doing on an evening out? Why?

  👍⭕👎   What elements of a social event make you frustrated? Disappointed? Angry? Uncomfortable?

  👍⭕👎   If you could go to any "high society" event in the world, which would you most enjoy? Why?

  👍⭕👎   If we were given $5,000 to go somewhere just for fun, where would you want to go? Why?

  👍⭕👎   If we had $500 to spend on an evening out, how would you want to spend it?

  👍⭕👎   If we had only $20 to do something "wild and crazy" together, what would you want to do?

👍⭕👎 When going out, what do you enjoy doing most with
another couple or small group of people?

👍⭕👎 If we were to go to dinner on three separate evenings with
three different married couples, what three couples
would you enjoy most?

👍⭕👎 How many evenings a week (or a month) would you enjoy
socializing with friends as a married couple? Why?

👍⭕👎 How do you feel about us each having time with the
"boys" / "girls"? How often?

- **Parties**

  👍⭕👎   How do you feel about parties?

  What kind do you most enjoy? Least enjoy? Want to avoid
  at all costs? Do you want us to have parties? How
  often? How many people?

  👍⭕👎   What is the best party you've ever attended? Why did you
  enjoy it?

  👍⭕👎   What kind of parties do you find most enjoyable
  (theme parties, costume parties, Valentine parties,
  Christmas parties, etc.)? Why?

- **Past Relationships**

 👍⭕👎   What do you think my future relationship should be with

 friends of the opposite sex

 (friendships I had prior to marriage)? (Name each one

 specifically, especially past romantic relationships,

 and discuss each of your assumptions about those

 relationships.)

 👍⭕👎   If you could go back in history, what social event would

 you enjoy most attending? Why?

- **Social Confidence / Comfort**

    👍 ⚪ 👎   How confident are you socially, on a scale of one to ten
    (1 = extremely insecure and 10 = extremely confident)?
    How does your confidence at a party change when we are
    there together, as compared to your being there alone?

    👍 ⚪ 👎   Do you like socializing and meeting a lot of new people
    or prefer going out with a very small group of friends?

    👍 ⚪ 👎   What are the social situations in which you feel least
    comfortable and why?

    👍 ⚪ 👎   What are the social situations in which you feel most
    confident and why?

    👍 ⚪ 👎   On a Friday or Saturday night,
    if the choice was between staying home and reading (or
    watching TV), or going out to a movie or party,
    which would you honestly prefer?

• **Travel**

👍○👎 How do you feel about having out-of-town friends
stay overnight with us? Out-of-town relatives?

👍○👎 How do you feel about staying with friends when we travel
(as opposed to staying in hotels)?

👍○👎 If we were to take a trip with another couple within five
hundred miles of home, what would you want to do? How
long would you want to stay? Where would you want to
go? With whom?

👍○👎 If we were to go to a foreign country with a couple what
country would you choose?
With whom? Why?

Remember:

Be very careful the friends you choose – for in fact you will be come more and more like them!

Friendships are invaluable! Social times are priceless!

Are you making the same assumptions about your social life?

Do you really enjoy the same people, the same parties, or entertaining in the same way?

How do you see your social life changing after saying, "I Do!"

7. SPIRITUAL

Politics and religion are two taboos of polite conversation.

In marriage, however, these topics are "must discussions!"

Take some time and discuss each of these questions as openly as possible.

Ten years from now, you will be very pleased you did!

For centuries, this is one area where couples have been shocked after saying, "I Do". It is often shocking to hear what a fiancé actually believes about God, Truth, Eternity. But, all of life is built on one's assumptions about spiritual realities. Please be as candid as possible with each other in this section. It is critical to your marriage and to future generations of your family.

- **Bible**

    👍⭕👎   How often do you read the Bible?

    👍⭕👎   How often would you like us to read the Bible together?
    Why?

- **Church**

  👍⭕👎 How do you feel about the church in general?

  👍⭕👎 How often do you want to attend church after we are married?

  👍⭕👎 What do you enjoy doing or being involved in at church?

  👍⭕👎 What type of worship service do you prefer?

  👍⭕👎 Is there a specific church or denomination that is important to you? Why?

  👍⭕👎 Is there a specific church or denomination you would not want to be involved with? Why?

• **Prayer**

    👍⭕👎 When you lean back in your chair and imagine heaven, what do you see?

    👍⭕👎 What does prayer mean to you?

    👍⭕👎 Would you want to pray together?

    👍⭕👎 How do you feel about our having a devotional time together? Why?

- **Questions Of God?**

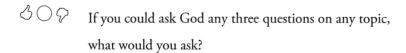 If you could ask God any three questions on any topic, what would you ask?

- **Spiritual Life**

   👍 ○ 👎   What are three highlights of your spiritual life?

   👍 ○ 👎   What was a low point of your spiritual life?

   👍 ○ 👎   How strong are (were) your parents' spiritual convictions?

   👍 ○ 👎   What would you like to see be different spiritually in our marriage and family compared to your parent's?

- **Tithe**

  👍⭕👎 Do you tithe (give 10 percent of your income) regularly to your church?

  👍⭕👎 Do you plan to continue tithing after marriage?

  👍⭕👎 Do you think a tithe is based on net or gross income?

  👍⭕👎 Do you think all of the tithe must go to the local church?

- **Truth**

  👍⭕👎 Is the church you (we) attend teaching the truths of the
         Bible?

  👍⭕👎 To you, what are some important, non-negotiable,
         Biblical issues, principles, or doctrines? Why?

- **Your Personal Beliefs**

  👍⭕👎 What do you believe the Bible says about marriage and divorce?

  👍⭕👎 How do you feel about and think about Jesus?

  👍⭕👎 In what area of your spiritual life do you feel the greatest need for personal growth?

  👍⭕👎 From your perspective, what are three keys to a strong spiritual life? Why?

  👍⭕👎 What are your beliefs about hell? About heaven? Why?

  👍⭕👎 How confident are you right now of your eternal salvation?

👍⭕👎   What do you believe is God's standard regarding sexual relationships prior to marriage? ... within marriage? ... outside of marriage?

👍⭕👎   When making a major decision, how do you personally determine God's will?

👍⭕👎   From a Biblical perspective, what do you believe to be the husband's responsibility to his wife?

To his children? To the spiritual welfare of his wife and children?

In each area, what are examples of practical ways you see this responsibility being carried out in our marriage?

👍⭕👎   From a Biblical perspective, what do you believe to be the wife's responsibility to her husband?

To her children? To the spiritual welfare of her husband and children?

In each area, what are examples of practical ways you see this responsibility being carried out in our marriage?

Remember:

Politics and religion are two taboos of polite conversation.

In marriage, however, these topics are "must discussions!"
Take some time and discuss each of these questions as openly as possible.

Ten years from now, you will be very pleased you did!

APPENDIX

A. Turning Disagree Answers To Agree ... Seeking Wise Advise

If a Disagree answer is one of significance to either one of you, there is more than one conflict-resolution skill or approach available. We will not list all of them for you. Our objective is to give you a few ideas on how to approach the conflict. They may or may not work for every Differences or Disagree issue, but you should be able to make headway toward an Agree.

If these ideas do not work, we suggest you seek a wise friend or a qualified minister or counselor. Tell the person what you have discussed about the issue.

Never be concerned or embarrassed about seeking qualified help. Your marriage is a precious asset and should be nurtured and cared for with wisdom. Marriage often takes more wisdom than any two people alone can provide.

Unfortunately, many times, either the husband or wife won't even consider talking to a counselor until one announces he or she is leaving the relationship. Then the reluctant one is willing to talk, but in many cases, it is too little, too late.

B. Marriage is a *Covenant* Relationship Not a *Contract* – John F. Huff

A *covenant* is based on trust between
two parties.
A *contract* is based on distrust between
two parties.

A *covenant* has unlimited responsibilities
A *contract* on mutually agreed limited
responsibilities.

A *covenant* cannot be broken when
different circumstances occur.
A *contract* can be voided by mutual
consent and divorced.

Our relationship with Jesus Christ
is based on a *covenant*.
Your relationship in marriage
is based on a *covenant*.

C. Top Ten Simple Ways To Predict A Problem Marriage

1. Getting married to spite someone else
2. Getting married without listening to close friends who are warning you of obvious problems
3. Getting married to someone with a different faith
4. Getting married with concerns and questions you are afraid to ask your friend or fiancé
5. Getting married with things you are hiding from your friend or fiancé you plan to disclose once the "knot has been tied"
6. Getting married on the rebound-within months of a painful breakup
7. Getting married because you just want to get out of your parents' house
8. Getting married without dating at least twelve months (may not be true for older couples).
9. Getting married based primarily on a relationship of correspondence or on line dating
10. Getting married because of a fear of never having another chance or just wanting to have children

These ten warning signs are not guaranteed to end in divorce. Some marriages make it in spite of built-in problems. But these are common situations which create major problems and pressures on a marriage and often end in divorce.

If you are in one of the top ten predictable problem marriage situations, it is doubly important you take this book very seriously.

D. Keeping Your Marriage Healthy And Happy

The following ten thoughts will help keep you focused on developing a healthy, happy, long-term marriage.

1. Commit "till death do us part"

    — you have made a vow to God and to another much-loved human being.

    • Dream together-look forward to things
    • Be loyal to your mate at all costs.
    • Care more about what your mate thinks of you than what your friends do.
    • Avoid getting caught up in the small issues and be committed to settling the big ones with love and prayer.

2. Develop a common spiritual commitment.

    • Pray for your mate regularly
    • Pray together regularly
    • Worship and read together

3. Want what is best for your life mate –

    even if it may be at the cost of your own comfort or interests.

- Focus on what's right with your mate, not what's wrong with him / her
- Work as a team. Rely on each other's strength
- Serve your mate

4. Spend time with model couples who have been happily married ten to twenty years longer than you.

- Develop a relationship with a personal mentor to help in tough times
- Spend time with peer couples that have healthy, happy marriages

5. Understand no marriage is perfect and no partner is perfect. Give grace to be different.

- No one wants to fail. Your mate is doing the best he / she can at the moment.
- Don't take all emotional explosions personally.
- Sometimes your mate just needs to let off steam!

6. Let your relationship breathe.
- A couple needs time together and away.
- When things get tense, you may just need a few hours or days away.
- Find time to communicate-walking on the beach, traveling together.

7. "Communicate!"
    - Listen to your mate's heart, not just to words.
    - Let your mate vent emotions without feeling you have to "fix it"!
    - Settle Differences!

8. Don't pout. Stay and talk it out.

    - "Clarify" your concerns if you don't like to "confront."
    - Listen carefully.
    - Allow the other to complete his / her thoughts without you interrupting, moving off the subject, or waiting impatiently to make your point.

9. Develop common interests

    - Enjoy hobbies and friends
    - Do fun things together—concerts, plays, picnics.
    - Travel together whenever you get a chance.

10. Get to know your mate at the deepest level possible.

    - Study your mate—what turns her / him off and on sexually, nonverbal signals, foreplay, moods.
    - Know precisely what your mate needs from you.

E. Avoid:

- Negative kidding
  – saying negative things you don't really mean secretly hurt and do serious damage to one's confidence and one's natural love;

- Conditional love - basing your love on actions of any kind;

- Waiting for your mate to meet your needs before you will meet hers/his;

- Talking negatively about your mate's parents.

F. Rekindling Your Romance

- Be romantic, not just sexy.

- Splurge occasionally.

- Do small things which communicate "Thinking only of you... Thought of you while I was away... You are the center of my universe!"

- Talk with a loving, caring, tender tone in your voice, not an angry, harsh, bitter tone

G. You Can Know You Are Going To Heaven When You Die!
– Tom Stebbins

You Can KNOW

you are going to HEAVEN

when you die!

From my earliest childhood – in fact, beginning nine months before I was born! – I went to church. Yet the answer to where I would spend eternity somehow escaped me. Instead, an almost paralyzing fear of death gripped my heart.

One night I dreamt a tidal wave swept my family out to sea and I was drowning. Just as I went down for the final time, I awakened in a cold sweat and thought, "I'm not ready for eternity!"

Another time I was traveling aboard a troop ship, when suddenly a siren blasted a warning the ship was sinking. Everyone donned their life jackets and ran for the lifeboats. My heart almost stopped, for fear of where I was really headed! But thankfully, I learned it was just a fire drill.

Years later these fearful episodes ended, when someone told me I didn't have to wonder about my final destination; it is possible to know for certain I will spend eternity with God in heaven! Acting on that news changed my life. The fear was gone, and in its place were joy, peace and courage in the face of death. Best of all, I had a deep assurance I would spend eternity with God in heaven.

How differently I have reacted since then; for instance, when I was in Vietnam — a place where I stared death in the face daily. The day that country fell to the communists, I left in a Marine helicopter from the roof of the U.S. Embassy. People all around me were screaming and scrambling for safety, but because of the marvelous assurance of knowing where I would spend eternity, I felt amazingly calm and stable.

Let me ask you a couple of questions.

Do you know for certain where you will spend eternity?

Will it be in heaven?

If God were to ask you, "Why should I let you into my heaven?", what would you say?

If you are unsure, or hesitate for even a moment to answer these questions, the few minutes it will take you to read the following information can make all the difference in your future! God says in his Word, the Holy Bible, "I write these things to you...that you may know that you have eternal life." (See 1 John 5:13.) How can we know that?

Find Him

There is a worldwide problem called sin. Everyone sins. The Bible says, "All have sinned and fall short of the glory of God." (See Romans 3:23.) Sin is transgressing God's law, and includes such things as lying, cheating, deceit, stealing, evil thoughts, immoral behavior, and more.

Have you ever wondered just how good you would have to be to make it to heaven? God said, "Be perfect therefore, just as your heavenly Father is perfect." (See Matthew 5:48.) Since it is impossible to be perfect, even the smallest sin disqualifies us from heaven. We can't be good enough, so there must be an entirely different way to get there!

God is merciful and does not want to punish us. He says, "I have loved you with an everlasting love." (See Jeremiah 31:3.) But the same Bible that tells us God loves us, also tells us God is perfectly just. So He must punish sin. He "does not leave the guilty unpunished." (See Exodus 34:7b).

God solved this problem in the Person of Jesus Christ. Who would you say Jesus is? The Bible teaches Jesus is God. He is "the visible expression of the invisible God." Anyone who wants to know what God is like can find out in the perfect and sinless life of Jesus.

He died on the cross and rose from the dead to pay the penalty for our sins, and to purchase a place for us in heaven, which He offers as a free gift. Does everyone receive this gift? No.

This gift is received by faith. Saving faith is the key that opens the door to eternal life in heaven. It is not a blind leap in the dark. It is not just head knowledge. Nor is it just a temporary belief. Saving faith is trusting in Jesus Christ alone for eternal life. It means resting upon Jesus alone, and on what He has done, rather than in anything we can do for ourselves to gain heaven. "For God so loved the world that He gave His only Son, that whoever believes in Him shall not perish but have eternal life." (See John 3:16.)

Would you like to receive God's gift of eternal life? Because this is so important, let's clarify what it involves.

Trust Him

It means you accept Christ as your Savior. Open the door to your heart and invite Him in. He says, "I stand at the door and knock. If anyone hears my voice and opens the door, I will come in." (See Revelation 3:20.) It means you also need to receive Him as Lord of your life, giving Him the "driver's seat" of your life, not the "back seat."

It means you need to repent – that is, to be willing to turn from anything that is not pleasing to God. He will tell you what He wants you to do as you grow in your relationship with Him, and will give you the strength to do it.

Now, if this is what you really want, you can receive this gift of eternal life through Jesus Christ, right where you are. "For it is with your heart that you believe and are justified, and it is with your mouth that you confess and are saved." (See Romans 10:10.)

You can pray right now and receive eternal life. Use your own words to pray, or use this prayer:

> *Jesus Christ, I know I am sinful and do not deserve eternal life.*
>
> *I believe you died and rose from the grave to purchase a place in heaven for me.*
>
> *Lord, come into my heart. Take control of my life. Forgive my sins.*
>
> *I confess them, and now place my trust in You for salvation.*
>
> *I accept your free gift of eternal life, and I thank You for it.*

If this prayer expresses what you believe in your heart, Jesus promises you this: "I tell you the truth, he who believes has eternal life."

Now you can know you have eternal life. And if you have truly turned away from your sins, placed your trust in Jesus Christ's sacrificial death, and received the gift of eternal life, you are now a child of God! Forever! "Yet all who received Him, to those who believed in His name, to them He gave the right to become children of God."

Welcome to God's family! So what's next?

Follow Him

Read the Bible, starting with the gospel of John. Read a chapter a day. "As newborn babes, desire the pure milk of the word (of God), that you may grow thereby." (See 1 Peter 2:2).

Pray. Spend time each day talking with God. "Do not be anxious about anything, but in everything, by prayer and petition, with thanksgiving, present your requests to God." (See Philippians 4:6-7.)

Worship God at a church that honors Jesus Christ and teaches you to love Him and His Word more. "God is a Spirit, and they that worship Him must worship Him in spirit and in truth." (See John 4:24.)

Spend time with other Christians who will help you grow in the faith. "And they devoted themselves to the apostles' teaching and fellowship, to the breaking of bread and the prayers." (See Acts 2:42.)

Tell others what Jesus means to you! "But you will receive power when the Holy Spirit comes on you, and you will be my witnesses." (See Acts 1:8.)

May God bless you abundantly!

Tom Stebbins

H. Conclusion

Express your thoughts and feelings openly yet sensitively. You cannot resolve a difference if you choose to be passive or silent.

Commit to the resolution of the disagreement and work on it. You cannot resolve a difference if one partner chooses to be less than 100 percent involved in making it work.

Realize the importance of the resolution of serious conflict. You can certainly live together without every single issue resolved, but your relationship will be weakened and possibly vulnerable to other problems or temptations.

These questions have been designed to help you make a wise decision. We want what is best for both of you. It is our prayer these questions helped you see that your potential mate will be your lifelong friend and spouse. We feel honored you let us be a part of your decision-making process.

Remember, this book is intended to maximize your marriage, not undermine it. Although some of the questions may seem threatening, look at them as an opportunity to learn more about yourself as well as your partner. As you both have a better understanding of each other, you will be able to handle the stresses that inevitably come in a marriage.

> We are not for or against your getting married.
>
> We are for your getting married –
>
>> if it will last the rest of your life.
>
> We are against your getting married –
>
>> if it will not bring you a mutually satisfying
>>
>> relationship, and end in divorce.

Choosing your life partner is, one of the three most critical decisions you will ever make. In order to make the right decision, you both must work carefully, taking the time to clarify assumptions.

Remember: It's far easier to stop a dating relationship or even an engagement today than it is to go through a divorce tomorrow!

Disagreements on basic issues – unresolved Disagree issues – need not be relationship breakers. You may just need help sorting out assumptions, understanding motivations, and clearing up communication. Don't hesitate to seek the help of a counselor to work through these differences. After all, a lifetime commitment is at stake.

These questions are not for one-time use. You can go through most of them once a year for the rest of your life and have fresh answers and gain new insights each time.

Your marriage should be based on a relationship which is secure, lasting, and mutually beneficial. It is our prayer that these questions help you make a wise and loving decision!

Invite us to your fiftieth anniversary party!

Bobb and Cheryl Biehl – Married August 22, 1964